MINI BIBL

The Story of Moses

Bethan James and Honor Ayres

Egypt was the land of the pyramids and of kings called Pharaohs.

God's people had gone to live there when Joseph was alive and for a long time, it was their home.

ODD ONE OUT

Which picture is the odd one out?

A   B

THE KING

These are pyramids built as tombs for the Egyptian kings.

What is the name for an Egyptian king?

C

D

3

Many years after Joseph had died, a cruel king lived in Egypt. He saw that there were too many of God's people in his land so he made them his slaves. He worked them hard and treated them badly.

4

WHO'S THE MAN?

Find the man in each row that matches the men in the big picture and write the numbers in the boxes.

1   2   3   4   5

1   2   3   4   5

SOMETHING'S WRONG

Find and circle three things that are wrong in this picture.

There was a very big river in Egypt called the Nile. Papyrus reeds grew along its banks and lots of creatures bathed in its waters. The cruel king told his soldiers to throw all the slaves' baby boys into the River Nile to drown! That way, there would be fewer boys to grow up into men and form an army against him.

IN THE RIVER

How many of these eight creatures might you find in a river?

WHICH RIVER?

What is the name of the very big river in Egypt?

TRUE OR FALSE?

Tick the right answer.

The papyrus reeds that grow by the river were used to make:

1 clocks

2 paper

3 weapons

4 ink

Miriam's mother did not want the soldiers to hurt her baby son. She hid him inside a basket and put it by the river bank. Miriam hid and watched.

WHO IS THIS?

This is Moses' big sister secretly watching over the basket.

What was her name?

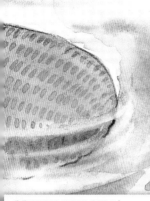

When one of the king's daughters came to the river to bathe, she saw the basket and found the baby.

'I want to keep him!' the princess said. 'I will call him Moses.'

WHICH PENCIL?

Select the right pencil to answer each of the questions about the picture of the baby.

1 Which pencil was used to colour in the basket?

2 Which pencil was used to colour in the water?

3 Which pencil was used to colour in the baby's face?

4 Which pencil was used to colour the baby's cheeks?

A B C D E

Moses grew up safely in the palace. When he was a man, God spoke to him from a burning bush and said, 'Go to the king and tell him to let my people go!'

Moses took his brother Aaron with him. But the king would not let God's people go.

FILL THE HOLE

Which detail fits into which space in the big picture?

WHICH PENCIL?

A B C D
         E

Select the right pencil to answer each of the questions about the picture above.

1 Which pencil was used to colour in the king's throne?

2 Which pencil was used to colour the plant pots?

3 In the picture above, which pencil was used to colour Moses' head covering?

So the land of Egypt suffered nine terrible plagues: frogs and flies and boils and locusts and ... all sorts of horrible things! But still the king would not let God's people go.

HOW MANY FROGS?

How many frogs are there in the picture below?

HOW MANY LOCUSTS?

Here is a great big locust. How many more little locusts can you find on these two pages?

Before the tenth plague, God's people ate one last meal, the Passover meal, and when the king said 'Go!' ... God's people went.

God helped them to cross the Red Sea by making a path through the water. God's people were slaves no more.

COLOUR IT IN

The king said GO. Colour in the letters.

IN OR OUT?

Which two of these picture fragments cannot be found in the picture above?

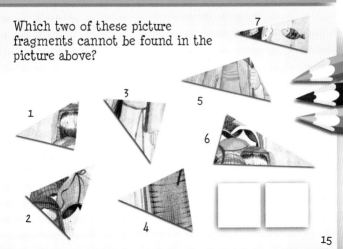

1

2

3

4

5

6

7

Answers

Page 2 ODD ONE OUT
C

Page 3 THE KING
Pharaoh

Page 5 WHO'S THE MAN?
2; 2

Page 5 SOMETHING'S WRONG

Page 6 IN THE RIVER
3

Page 7 WHICH RIVER?
Nile

Page 7 TRUE OR FALSE?
1 false, 2 true, 3 false, 4 false

Page 8 WHO IS THIS?
Miriam

Page 9 WHICH PENCIL?
1 A; 2 E; 3 B; 4 D

Page 10 FILL THE HOLE
A 4; B 3; C 1; D 5; E 2

Page 11 WHICH PENCIL?
1 A; 2 E; 3 C

Page 12 HOW MANY FROGS?
13

Page 13 HOW MANY LOCUSTS?
8

Page 15 IN OR OUT?
1 and 5

First edition 2015

Copyright © 2015 Anno Domini Publishing
www.ad-publishing.com

Text copyright © 2015 Bethan James
Illustrations copyright © 2015 Honor Ayres

Published 2015 by CWR, Waverley Abbey House,
Waverley Lane, Farnham, Surrey, GU9 8EP, UK
Registered Charity No. 294387
Registered Limited Company No. 1990308
For a list of national distributors, visit
www.cwr.org.uk/distributors

Printed and bound in China

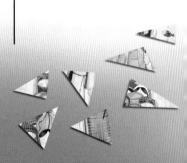

Beginner's Guide to
GERMAN

Illustrated by Rebecca Archer

© 1992 Henderson Publishing Limited

Woodbridge, England

BEGINNER'S GUIDE TO GERMAN

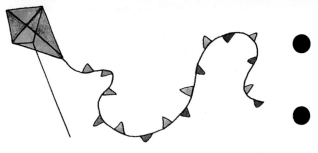

If you are learning German at school you will find that these pages are a great help. They are not meant to be a complete German course but an aid to help you through the early stages of learning the language.

BEGINNER'S GUIDE TO GERMAN

A Basic Guide To German - Masculine, Feminine and Neuter

Remember that in German nouns are either masculine, feminine or neuter. Instead of one word for 'the', we must choose from 3 words:

Masculine:	**der**
Feminine:	**die**
Neuter:	**das**

You can guess the gender of some words, like **der Mann** - the man, or **die Frau** - the woman, but who could guess the gender for a word like child ? In German it is neuter, **das Kind**. Where you see (f) beside a noun, it tells you it is feminine, (m) masculine and (n) neuter. Where (pl) appears, it is a plural noun.

The plural for all three genders is "die", so **die Blumen** are the flowers. Note that word endings change in the plural. Remember too, that all German nouns begin with a capital letter.

The word 'a', or 'an' also agrees with the gender of the noun, like **ein Mann**, **eine Frau** and **ein Kind** - but we can't tell if a child is a boy or a girl from these two words.

BEGINNER'S GUIDE TO GERMAN

andere other
schön beautiful
ungeheuer enormous
gut good
nett nice
gross big
jung young
hübsch pretty
lang long
schlecht bad
klein small
alt old

Vowels and Umlauts

Umlauts are two dots sometimes seen over the vowels a, o and u which change the vowel sound. Umlauts often occur in plural nouns as in **das Haus** - the house, **die Häuser** - the houses.

BASIC WORDS

Some words are used often in sentences and to ask questions. If you learn these now, you can use them throughout the pages which follow.

es ist ...it is ...
Was ist das? What is that?
Was ist ...? What is ... ?
auch also
Guten Tag Hello
Wie geht's? How are you?
gut good, well
sehr gut very good
genug enough
ganz gut quite well
nicht so gut not so well
schlecht awful

sie they (plural for all genders)
es gibt there is
es sind there are
ja yes
nein no
niemals never
vielleicht perhaps
manchmal sometimes

NUMBERS

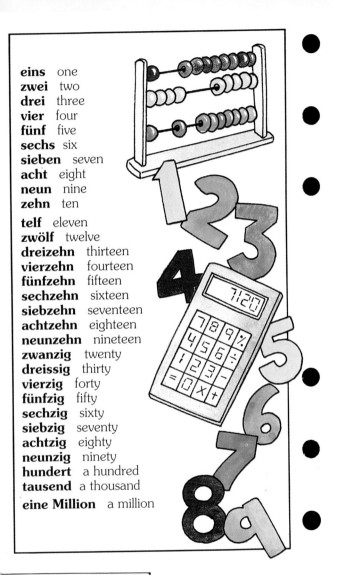

eins	one
zwei	two
drei	three
vier	four
fünf	five
sechs	six
sieben	seven
acht	eight
neun	nine
zehn	ten
telf	eleven
zwölf	twelve
dreizehn	thirteen
vierzehn	fourteen
fünfzehn	fifteen
sechzehn	sixteen
siebzehn	seventeen
achtzehn	eighteen
neunzehn	nineteen
zwanzig	twenty
dreissig	thirty
vierzig	forty
fünfzig	fifty
sechzig	sixty
siebzig	seventy
achtzig	eighty
neunzig	ninety
hundert	a hundred
tausend	a thousand
eine Million	a million

ALL ABOUT YOU

ein Junge   a boy

Ich heisse Paul. Wie heisst Du?

ein Mädchen a girl	**der Arm** arm
der Kopf head	**der Finger** finger
das Haar hair	**der Daumen** thumb
die Haut skin	**die Hand** hand
das Auge eye	**das Bein** leg
die Nase nose	**das Knie** knee
der Mund mouth	**die Zehe** toe
die Zähne teeth	**der Fuss** foot
die Brust chest	**der Knöchel** ankle

What is he saying?
My name is Paul.
What's your name?

ALL ABOUT YOU

die Locken
curly hair
der Pony a fringe
er trägt eine Brille
he wears glasses
blonde Haare
fair hair
der Hund dog
komisch funny

er wedelt den Schwanz
it wags its tail
die Katze the cat
der Mann the man
schnurren to purr
freundlich friendly
der Schnurrbart
moustache

Wie alt bist Du, Sophie?

Ich bin acht Jahre alt.

Ich heisse Marc. Ich bin so alt, wie Sophie.

What are they saying?
Paul: How old are you, Sophie?
Sophie: I am eight years old.
Marc: My name is Marc. I am the same age as Sophie.

THE FAMILY

die Familie the family
der Vater father
die Mutter mother
die Schwester sister
der Bruder brother
der Grossvater grandfather
die Grossmutter grandmother
der Onkel uncle
der Vetter boy cousin
die Kusine girl cousin

What are they saying?
Sophie: Here is my family.
Grandmother: She is my granddaughter.
Aunt: She is my niece. The baby is my nephew.

Note: How to say '**My**': Use **mein** for 'der' nouns, like mein Kopf, **meine** for 'die' nouns, like meine Mutter,

and **mein** for 'das' nouns, like mein Haar. To say 'My ...' plus a plural noun, say **meine** as in meine Eltern (my parents). The endings change sometimes, so just listen out for that stem, *mein...*

FAMILY EVENTS

die Geburt birth
die Hochzeit
wedding
geboren werden to
be born
die Braut bride
die Mutti Mum
der Bräutigam
bridegroom
der Vati Dad
die Party party
das Geschenk gift
der Kuchen cake
die goldene
Hochzeit
golden wedding

What are they saying?
Baby: Waaaah! - it's the same in any language!
Wedding guest: Congratulations
Grandma at birthday party: Happy birthday!
Grandpa at golden wedding: Thank you very much.
Guests at birthday party: Hello.

THINGS PEOPLE DO

der Matrose sailor
der Soldat soldier
das Mannequin
model

der Arzt doctor
**der
Geschäftsinhaber**
shopkeeper
der Pastor
clergyman
der Arbeiter
labourer

der Rechtsanwalt
solicitor
der Polizeibeamte
policeman
der Müllmann
dustman

der Lastwagenfahrer
lorry driver
der Taxifahrer
taxi driver

THINGS PEOPLE DO

der Feuerwehrmann
fireman
der Friseur hairdresser
der Bauer farmer

der Koch cook
der Bankmanager
bank manager
der Briefträger
postman

der Kassierer
cashier (male)
die Kassiererin
cashier (female)

der Schauspieler
actor
**die
Schauspielerin**
actress
der Dirigent
musical conductor

THE HOUSE

das Dach roof
das Haus house
der Häuserblock block of flats
die Etagenwohnung flat
der Balkon balcony
die Haustür front door
der Schornstein chimney

klingeln to ring the bell
die Klingel the bell
der Nachbar neighbour (male)
die Nachbarin neighbour (female)
das Fenster window

Ich wohne in diesem Haus. Wo wohnt ihr?

Ich wohne in einer Etagenwohnung.

Ich auch.

What are they saying?
Paul: I live in this house. Where do you live?
Sophie: I live in a flat.
Marc: Me too.

NOTE: How to say 'this':
Like the word **mein**, you will hear the stem **diese** (this) with different endings.

THE KITCHEN

die Küche kitchen
die Waschmaschine washing machine
spülen to wash up
bügeln to iron
schmutzig dirty
das Spülbecken sink
waschen to wash

der Schrank cupboard
das Glas glass
das Brot bread
der Tee tea
die Tasse cup
die Gabel fork
das Messer knife
der Löffel spoon

Diese Teller sind jetzt sauber, Mutti.

Gut, Paul.

What are they saying?
Paul: These plates are clean, now, Mum.
Mother: Good, Paul.

THE LIVING ROOM

das Wohnzimmer living room

der Fernsehapparat
television

der Videorekorder
video

die Gardinen
curtains

die Uhr clock

die Heizung radiator

das Sofa sofa

der Sessel armchair

das Feuer fire

bei dem Feuer sitzen
to sit by the fire

das Buch book
der Tisch table
der Teppich carpet
der Fussboden
floor

THE BEDROOM

das **Schlafzimmer**
bedroom
das **Bett** bed
der **Wecker** alarm clock

What are they saying?
Father: Good night, Paul.
Paul: But Dad, I'd like a glass of water, please.

---

der **Morgenrock**
dressing gown
der **Pullover** jumper
das **Hemd** shirt
die **Hose** trousers
schlafen gehen to go to sleep
der **Schlafanzug**
pyjamas
die **Pantoffeln**
slippers
das **Oberbett** duvet
schlafen to sleep
träumen to dream

THE BATHROOM

das Badezimmer bathroom
baden to have a bath
spritzen to splash
die Waage scales
der Stöpsel plug
die Seife soap
die Zahnbürste tooth-brush
Zähne putzen to clean your teeth
der Wasserhahn the tap

das Wasser water
heisses Wasser hot water
kaltes Wasser cold water
die Zahnpasta toothpaste
der Rasierapparat razor
der Spiegel mirror
das Handtuch towel
die Dusche shower

THE GARDEN

der Garten garden
gärtnern
to do the gardening
der Rasen lawn
das Blumenbeet
flowerbed
der Rasenmäher
lawnmover
die Blume flower
das Unkraut weed

der Baum tree
der Vogel bird
das Gewächshaus
greenhouse
der Busch bush

Wo ist der Drachen, Paul?

Er ist verloren gegangen.

Wie schade!

What are they saying?
Marc: Where is the kite, Paul?
Paul: It's lost.
Sophie: What a shame!

GOING SHOPPING

das Kaufhaus
department store
die Rolltreppe
escalator
die Quittung
receipt
die Kundin female
customer

die Verkäuferin
female shop assistant
teuer expensive
das Spielzeug toy
die Kleidung clothes
kaufen to buy
der Preis the price

Ich möchte gern ..

Ja, bitte.

What are they saying?
Customer: I would like to buy ...
Assistant: Certainly.

SHOPPING FOR FOOD

die Metzgerei
butcher
**das Lebensmittel-
geschäft** grocer
die Bäckerei
bakery
der Fischmarkt
fishmonger
der Verkaufsstand
market stall

Schlange stehen
to stand in a queue
**das
Delikatessengeschäft**
delicatessen
die Konditorei
cake shop
der Supermarkt
supermarket

Ich habe eine Liste und eine Einkaufstasche.

What is she saying?
I have a list and a shopping bag.

UNPACKING THE SHOPPING

der Joghurt yoghurt

das Brot bread

die Milch milk

der Reis rice

der Pfeffer pepper

der Fisch fish

die Tomaten (f) tomatoes

der Apfel apple

die Eier (n) eggs

der Essig vinegar

die Bohnen (f) beans

das Salz salt

das Mehl flour

die Karotten (f) carrots

die Kartoffeln (f) potatoes

die Zitronen (f) lemons

AT THE POST OFFICE

das Postamt post office
das Paket parcel
der Brief letter
das Portemonnaie purse
die Handtasche handbag

der Briefkasten post box
das Geld money
die Luftpost air mail
das Formular form
die Briefmarke stamp
schicken to send

MAKING A PHONE CALL

telefonieren to make a telephone call
das Telefon the telephone
die Nummer wählen dial the number
die Telefonnummer telephone number

das Telefonbuch telephone directory
auf Wiederhören goodbye
auflegen to hang up
im Notfall in case of emergency
die Polizei rufen call for the police
Wo seid ihr? Where are you?

Hallo, wer ist am Apparat?

What is Sophie's Mum saying?
Hello ... Who is speaking?

ASKING THE WAY

Wie kommt man nach ...? Which way is ... ?
rechts right
links left
geradeaus straight on
abbiegen turn
nehmen to take
Ist es weit? Is it far?
neben next to
die Strasse the street
die erste Strasse the first street
die zweite Strasse the second street
die dritte Strasse the third street
die Kirche the church
dort drüben over there
Entschuldigen Sie, bitte Excuse me, please ...
Danke schön Thank you
Bitte sehr You are welcome

Ist die Kirche weit von hier?

Langsam, bitte!

Gehen Sie geradeaus bis zur Metzgerei, dann nehmen sie die zweite Strasse links, dann -

What are they saying?
Man: Is the church far from here?
Paul: Go straight on to the butcher's, then take the second street on the left, then ...
Woman: Slowly, please!

AT SCHOOL

der Kindergarten nursery school
die Grundschule primary school
die Schule high school
das Gymnasium high school
die Universität university

die Klasse classroom
der Rektor headmaster
der Kurs course
der Schüler (m) boy pupil
die Schülerin (f) girl pupil
in der Schule at school
lesen to read
schreiben to write
der Spielplatz playground
das Heft exercise book
die Stifttasche pencil case
das Lineal ruler
der Bleistift pencil

AT SCHOOL

das Quartal..term
der Quartal-Anfang
beginning of term
das Quartal-Ende
end of term
der Stundenplan
timetable
das Buchstabieren
spelling
das Wort word
der Satz sentence
das Informetik
computer studies
die Geschichte
history
die Erdkunde
geography
die Chemie
chemistry
die Physik physics
die Musik music
die Gymnastik
gymnastics
der Computer
computer
die Tastatur
keyboard

OUT IN THE CAR

der Verkehr traffic

der Wagen / das Auto car

das Fahrrad bicycle

der Omnibus coach

Einbahnstrasse! one way

keine Durchfahrt no entry

Parkverbot no parking

der Lastwagen lorry

das Motorrad motorbike
langsam slow
die Autobahn motorway
langsam fahren to slow down
der Verkehrsstau traffic jam

die Ampel traffic light

einen platten Reifen haben to have a flat tyre
eine Panne haben to break down

GOING BY TRAIN

der Zug the train
der Bahnhof station
der Fahrkartenschalter
ticket office
die Fahrkarte ticket
einen Platz reservieren to
reserve a seat
der Zugbegleiter
guard

pünktlich on time
der Schlafwagen
sleeping car
der Schnellzug
express train
der Inter-City Zug
inter-city train
das Gepäcknetz
luggage rack
der Bahnsteig
platform
das Gleis track
der Fahrplan
timetable

AT THE AIRPORT

der Flughafen
airport
das Flugzeug
aeroplane
fliegen to fly

das Handgepäck
hand luggage

die Stewardess air
hostess

der zollfreie Laden
duty free shop

der Anhänger
label

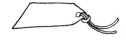

der Koffer suitcase
nichts zu verzollen
nothing to declare
der Zoll customs
der Zollbeamte
customs official
einsteigen to board
der Pilot pilot

der Kofferkuli
trolley

der Pass passport

TAKING THE FERRY

der Hafen port
die Fähre ferry
die Überfahrt
crossing
die Seekrankheit
sea sickness
laden to load
entladen to unload
der Schiffsraum
the hold
der Anker anchor

das Bullauge
porthole
mit dem Schiff
fahren travel by boat
das Deck deck
der Schornstein
funnel
die Laufplanke
gangway
der Kapitän captain

AT A CAFE

der Kellner waiter
die Speisekarte menu
die Rechnung bill
das Trinkgeld tip
das Tablett tray
eine Cola a cola
ein Glas Milch glass of milk
ein Eis ice-cream

heisse Trinkschokolade hot chocolate
Tee mit Milch tea with milk
Tee mit Zitrone tea with lemon
der Käse cheese
das Fleisch meat
die Pommes Frites chips
die Pizza pizza
der Salat salad

Was möchten Sie bestellen?

Einen Orangensaft und zwei Limonaden, bitte.

What are they saying?
Waiter: What would you like to order?
Paul: An orange juice and two lemonades, please.

FEELING POORLY

die Blumen (pl) flowers
erbrechen to be sick
eine Erkältung haben to have a cold
niesen to sneeze
hohes Fieber haben to have a high temperature
das Rezept prescription
die Tablette pill
ich fühle mich besser I feel better

Hallo, Marc. Hast Du Magenschmerzen?

Nein, ich habe Kopfschmerzen.

What are they saying?
Sophie: Hello, Marc. Have you got stomach-ache?
Marc: No, I have a headache.

THE TIME OF DAY

der Morgen morning
der Nachmittag afternoon
der Abend evening
die Nacht night
die Mitternacht midnight

Wie spät ist es? What time is it?
Es ist ein Uhr. It is one o'clock
Es ist fünf Uhr. It is five o'clock

Viertel vor sieben quarter to seven
zehn vor sieben ten to seven
fünf nach sieben five past seven
Viertel nach sieben quarter past seven
halb acht half past seven (half an hour before eight)

Es ist acht Uhr abends.
It is eight o'clock in the evening

THE WEATHER

der Winter winter

der Sommer summer
es regnet it's raining
es ist kalt it's cold
der Donner thunder
der Blitz lightning
der Regenbogen rainbow
der Hagel hail
der Frost frost

der Frühling spring

der Herbst autumn
der Schnee snow
Es ist mir heiss I'm hot
Es ist nebelig It's foggy
der Wind the wind
Es ist windig It's windy
Die Sonne scheint the sun is shining

Es ist schön.

Wie ist das Wetter?

What are they saying?
Sophie: What's the weather like?
Mother: It's fine.

THE DAY AND THE DATE

Wann hast du Geburtstag?

Januar January
Februar February
März March
April April
Mai May
Juni June
Juli July
August August
September September
Oktober October
November November
Dezember December

Mein Geburtstag ist am einundzwanzigsten April.

der Sonntag Sunday
der Montag Monday
der Dienstag Tuesday
der Mittwoch Wednesday
der Donnerstag Thursday
der Freitag Friday
der Samstag Saturday
der Sonnabend (also Saturday)

What are they saying?
Marc: What is the date of your birthday?
Sophie: My birthday is the twenty-first of April.

THE DAY AND THE DATE

der Tag day
die Woche week
der Monat month
das Jahr year
heute today
gestern yesterday
morgen tomorrow
vorgestern the day
before yesterday
übermorgen the
day after tomorrow
nächste Woche
next week
der nächste Tag
the next day
am nächsten Tag
the next day
nächsten Freitag
next Friday
der erste Mai the
first of May
**der zweite
November** the
second of November

AROUND THE WORLD

die Welt the world
der Norden north
der Süden south
der Westen west
der Osten east
der Nordpol North Pole
der Südpol South Pole
das Land country
der Kontinent continent
Grossbritannien Great Britain
die Schweiz Switzerland

Frankreich France
Deutschland Germany
die Niederlande Holland
Italien Italy
Spanien Spain
U.S.A. America
Russland Russia
Indien India
China China
Neuseeland New Zealand
Australien Australia
Südamerika South America

AT THE BEACH

am Strand at the seaside
die Sandburg sandcastle
der Eimer bucket
die Schaufel spade
der Felsen rock
der Krebs crab
die Muschel shell
die Möwe seagull
die Welle wave

schwimmen to swim
der Strand beach
planschen to paddle
das Wellenreiten to go windsurfing
die Sonnenbrille sunglasses

Zwei Mark.

Wieviel kostet ein Eis?

What are they saying?
Paul: How much is an ice-cream?
Man: Two marks.

AT THE ZOO

der Zoo the zoo
das wilde Tier
wild animal
das Zebra zebra
die Giraffe giraffe

**der junge
Seehund** baby
seal
der Pinguin
penguin

der Löwe lion
der Tiger tiger

das Kamel camel
der Strauss
ostrich

der Eisbär polar
bear

der Elefant
elephant
der Stosszahn
tusk
der Affe monkey

ON THE FARM

das Tor gate
der Weizen wheat
ernten to harvest
das Schaf sheep
der Schäferhund sheepdog
das Lamm lamb

das Feld field
der Bauer farmer
das Schwein pig
die Scheune barn
die Kuh cow
die Kühe melken to milk the cows

Jetzt noch nicht, Paul - in einer Woche.

Ist es Erntezeit, Grossvater?

What are they saying?
Paul: Is it harvest, Grandad?
Grandad: Not yet, Paul - in a week's

COLOURS

die Farbe colour
hell bright
trübe dull
blass pale
dunkel dark
rot red
blau blue
grün green
violett purple
orange orange
schwarz black
weiss white
grau grey
gelb yellow

MEASUREMENTS

die Grösse height
messen to measure
das Meter metre
die Weite width
die Länge length

der Rauminhalt
volume
ein Liter a litre
ein halbes Liter
half a litre

das Gewicht weight
ein halbes Kilo
half a kilo

die Form shape

der Kreis circle

das Dreieck triangle

das Viereck square

HOBBIES

ich stricke I knit

ich koche gern I like to cook

ich spiele Klavier I play the piano

ich treibe gern Sport I like to play sport

ich male I paint

ich tanze I dance

ich sehe gern fern I like to watch T.V.

ich lese Bücher I read books

EATING WITH FRIENDS

Bedien Dich selbst
Help yourself
Möchtest Du noch mehr ..? Would you like more ...?
Vielen Dank, ich habe genug Thank you, I have enough
es schmeckt sehr gut it is delicious

Bitte reich mir ..
Please pass me ...
viel Spass! Have fun
Es ist auf dem Tisch
It's on the table
es hat mir gut geschmeckt
I enjoyed that

What are they saying?
Mother: Enjoy your meal
Sophie: Thank you. I'm really hungry.

PRONOUNS

Personal pronouns

ich	I
du	you (for friends and family)
er	he
sie	she
es	it
wir	we
ihr	you
sie (pl)	they
Sie	You (being formal or polite)

Here are some simple phrases using these pronouns:

Ich bin müde I am tired

Du hast zwei Mark..You have two [Deutsch] marks.

Er ist alt He is old

Sie ist schön She is lovely

Es ist sehr langsam It is very slow

Fahren Sie heute? Are you travelling today?

USEFUL PHRASES

Es tut mir leid I am sorry
Ja, das stimmt Yes, that is right
schon gut all right

ich gehe nach Hause I am going home
zum ersten Mal for the first time

ich bin hier fremd I am a stranger here
ich weiss es nicht I don't know

... and some words you are bound to need!

schwierig difficult
krank ill
froh glad
prima! great!
einfach simple, easy or, one way

VERBS

Verbs are *doing* words. Here are a few important verbs to know. Learn the examples given to help you use them correctly. They are all written in the present tense. Notice how the stem of the verb changes when it applies to different subjects (people doing the verb).

haben - to have

ich **habe** Brot   I have bread
Du **hast** kein Geld   You have no money
er **hat** Eile   He is in a hurry
sie **hat** guten Appetit   She has a good appetite
wir **haben** keine Zeit   We have no time
ihr **habt** die Kleider   You have the clothes
sie **haben** die Taschen   They have the bags

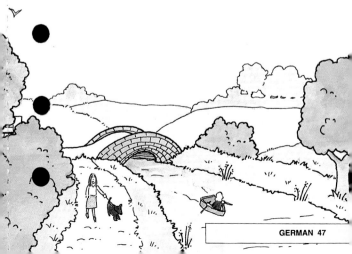

VERBS

sein -to be

ich **bin** müde   I am tired
Du **bist** krank   You are ill
er **ist** nicht da   He is not there
sie **ist** nett   She is nice
wir **sind** Touristen   We are tourists
ihr **seid** spät   You are late
sie **sind** im Zug   They are on the train

Some more verbs to recognise and learn:

lieben to like, or to love - **ich liebe die Musik**

machen to make, or to do -**ich mache Pizza heute**

laufen to walk or run - **er läuft geradeaus**

essen to eat -**essen Sie Salat?**